dalenbooks.com

First published in 2011 by
Dalen Books, Tresaith, Ceredigion SA43 2JH, Wales

ISBN 978-1-906587-25-3
Originally published in French by Casterman as *Louisette la Taupe: Mouton Circus*
Copyright © English adaptation, Dalen 2011
Copyright © 2007 Casterman, Brussels

Printed in Wales by Cambrian

BRUNO HEITZ

molly THE MOLE

Woolly

CIRCUS

DALEN

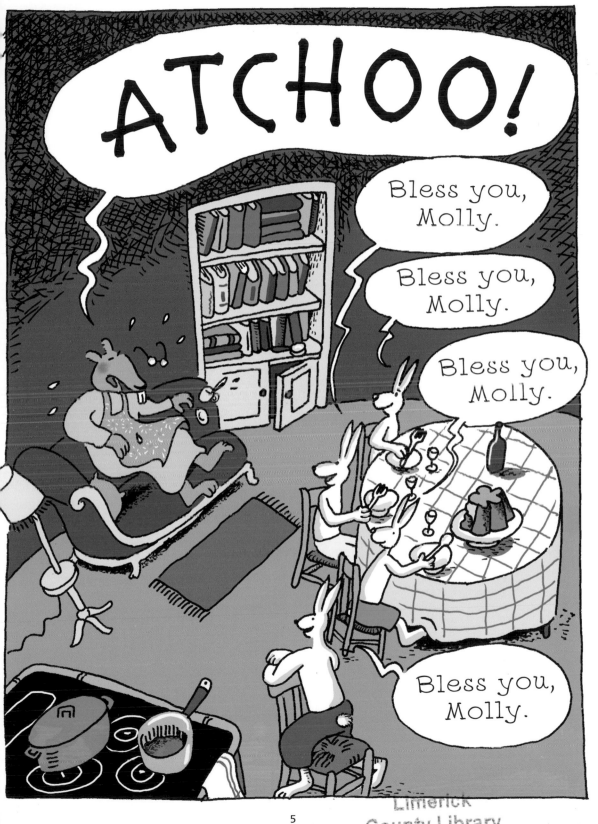

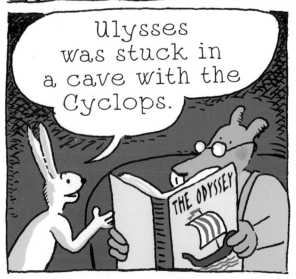

6

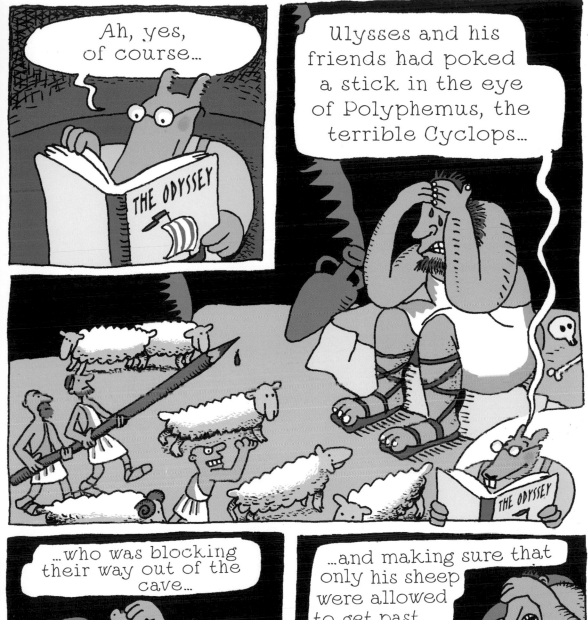

Then Ulysses had a bright idea!

He tied some of the sheep together...

...and told his men to hang on under their bellies.

Then, as Ulysses clung on to the belly of the biggest ram, he managed to escape and the Cyclops was none the wiser.

That's how they were able to get back to their ship and sail away...

ATCHOO!

!

THE ODYSSEY

Nothing serious!

But there is something in there making an extremely loud noise, like someone fast asleep and snoring!

Is there anything you can give her for this loud snoring noise?

Yes!

Lots of fresh air!

12

16

My clever chimp wasn't really brainy, so I sold him. My gymnastic goat jumped the fence and escaped...

Do you think it's fair to make a show of talented animals?

Goodness! You don't follow the other sheep, do you?!

No I don't! I have a mind of my own!

I can tell you what I think about lots of things, from cooking to politics, to... ATCHOO!... animal rights!

Well well!

And I thought you'd only be able to count up to 10 and sing "Baa Baa Black Sheep"…!

ATCHOO!

This is going to be fabulous! We'll go on tour and make a fortune!

WOOLLY CIR

Lots and lots of money!

On ONE condition!

?

That we go on tour up into the MOUNTAINS.

My health depends on it.

That shouldn't be a problem… Up a mountain or down by the sea, I can still make my fortune!

Say, now that we're working together, what's your name?

Call me Ulysses. And steady on the bottle… you're driving in the morning…

24

Miles and miles and miles away...

DOCTOR BADGER HOLLOW SET SURGERY.

!

COUNTRY TIMES

I must tell the rabbits!

It says, "Crowds give this incredible sheep called Ulysses a standing ovation in each and every venue after hearing its passionate speeches on the rights and wrongs of modern life...'

That's Molly!

What is she up to?

It's not like Molly to clown around like this!

I daresay she's far from coming home!

27